Brain
Stretchers

Using Deductive Reasoning to Problem Solve

Written by Linda Schwartz

Illustrated by Kelly Kennedy

The Learning Works, Inc.

The Learning Works

Illustrator: Kelly Kennedy

Editor: Eric Larson

Book design: Studio E Books, Santa Barbara, CA

Cover illustrator: Kelly Kennedy

Cover photograph: Photo by Bob Anderson/Masterfile

Cover designer: Barbara Peterson

Project director: Linda Schwartz

Contents

To the Teacher

Students are going to love these fun puzzlers that challenge their deductive reasoning skills. Each two-page activity contains whimsical illustrations along with clues that students eliminate one at a time until they find the answer that solves the puzzler.

Use these puzzlers at a learning center, for extra credit, or for students who finish their classwork ahead of the others and need an activity that doesn't require teacher involvement. Once they try one brain stretcher, students will be clamoring for more. Learning has never been more fun!

BRAIN STRETCHER AWARD

_____
(name)

has successfully completed
activities in deductive reasoning.

_____
(teacher)   (date)

Super Problem Solver AWARD

_____
(name)

For using deductive reasoning
to problem solve.

_____
(teacher)   (date)

The Dog Show

I liked the way the winning dog's soft, fluffy fur felt when I petted it.

The winning pooch doesn't have a tail that people can trip over.

I picked the dog that has an interesting pattern on its body.

I voted for the dog that was peppy and alert.

The dog I voted for has such a friendly face.

The winning dog doesn't look like it would fit inside a hot dog roll.

With that size nose, the winning pooch must have a great sense of smell!

The winning dog could mop the floor with its ears.

The winning dog would never be mistaken for a miniature horse.

6

Name _____

The Dog Show

The winner of the dog show is _____

7

Name _____

Samantha's New Hat

Samantha is shopping for a new hat and has definite ideas about what she wants to buy. Use the clues to eliminate one hat at a time until you find the one Samantha ends up buying.

I have such sensitive skin, and don't want too much sun to get on my face.

My new hat has to fit my rather large head.

I'd like the top of my new hat to have a soft, rounded curve.

Straw hats are "in" this season, and I definitely want to be in fashion.

I'm crazy about polka dots! I want my hat to have lots of polka dots.

My hat must remind me of my favorite hobby— gardening.

I don't want to spend more than $19.95 for my new hat.

My new hat must have something colorful, long, and flowing tied to it to soften its look.

Something on my new hat must remind me of my beloved pet parrot, Polly.

8

Name _____

Samantha's New Hat

How much money does Samantha's new hat cost? _____

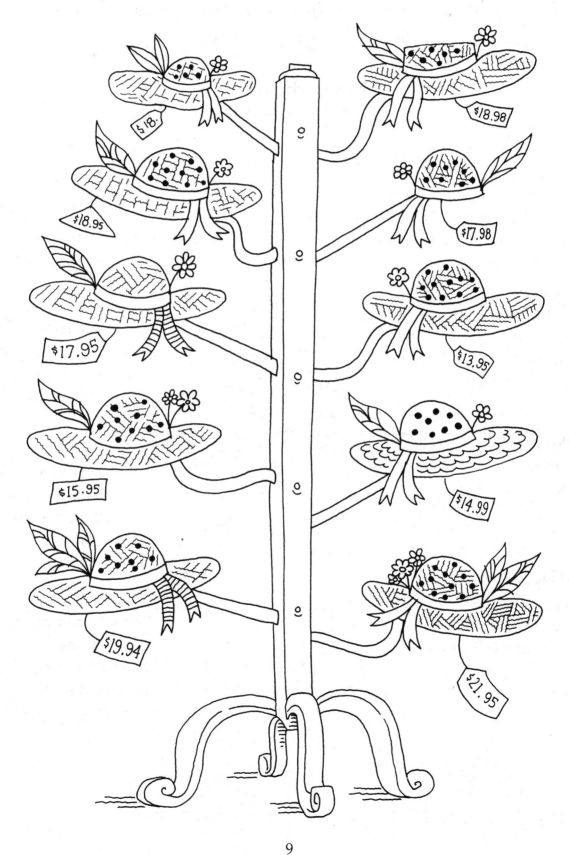

Name _____

For the Birds

Members of the local bird-watching club have just spotted a rare zzyzx bird! To discover which bird is the zzyzx, use the clues to eliminate one bird at a time.

Name _____

For the Birds

What number is the zzyzx bird? _____

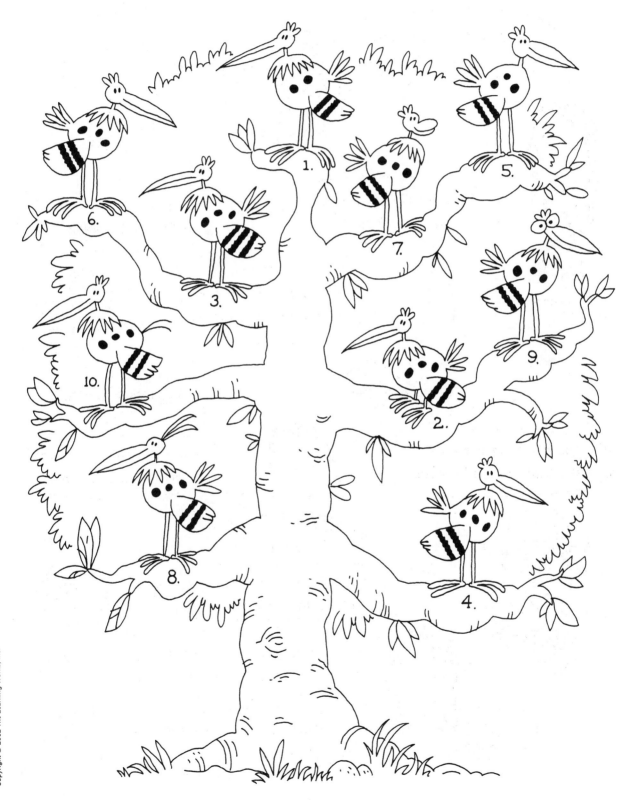

Name _____

Now Playing

A group of friends wants to go to a movie. But everyone has to agree on what movie to see.
Use the clues to eliminate one movie at a time until you find one the friends will all enjoy.

I get frightened easily and don't want to see a scary movie with monsters.

I don't like musicals with all that singing and dancing.

If I see another movie about dogs, I think I'll scream!

I don't like mushy love stories.

TICKETS

I don't like mysteries because I can never solve them.

I like to watch cartoons on television, not at the movies.

I don't like war movies or movies where people are fighting.

Science-fiction movies are not for me. I like more realistic movies.

Name _____

Now Playing

The movie the group finally goes to see is _____

13

Name _____

What's for Dessert?

Dad's in the kitchen making something delicious for dessert. Use the clues to
eliminate one dessert at a time and find out what he's making.

Dad is not making a dessert that has a warm chocolate sauce poured on top.

Dad's dessert doesn't use a red fruit with seeds on the outside.

The dessert Dad is making does not have icing on the top.

The dessert does not have a crust with fruit inside.

The dessert Dad is making is not a type of hard candy.

Dad's dessert isn't made with fruit, ice cream, and whipped cream.

The dessert Dad is making is not a dessert you can drink with a straw.

The dessert Dad is making is not made with fruit flavors and eaten frozen.

14

Name _____

What's for Dessert?

Dad's making _____

Cookies

Ice Cream Soda

Apple Pie

Chocolate Cake

Sherbet

Hot Fudge Sundae

Peanut Brittle

Banana Split

Strawberry Shortcake

15

Name _____

The Toy Store

Raul just bought something at the Valley Toy Store. Use the clues to eliminate one item at a time to discover what he bought.

I didn't buy anything that requires that I wear a helmet.

I didn't buy an item that uses marbles.

I didn't buy anything that requires glue.

My mom won't complain about the racket I'm making with the item I bought.

I didn't buy anything with hundreds of pieces that could easily get lost.

I didn't buy anything that's played outdoors or with a team.

I'm neat and tidy so I didn't buy anything that would get my hands or clothes messy.

I don't have a computer at home.

The item I bought is not a replica of a human figure.

16

Name _____

The Toy Store

Which of these toys did Raul buy? _____

Name _____

The Substitute Teacher

The sixth-graders at Brainy Elementary have a substitute teacher for the day. Find out the name of the substitute by using the students' clues to eliminate one teacher at a time.

The sub sure seems like a happy person!

She won't have to worry about the bright sun when we go out for P.E.

She sure doesn't need a perm!

I like her compact pocketbook.

I like the way she coordinated her outfit to match.

She sure loves flashy jewelry.

The substitute could be a basketball player.

She looks like she's going to give us a ton of homework!

How can she walk in those shoes and keep her balance?

18

Name _____

The Substitute Teacher

What is the name of the substitute teacher? _____

| Ms. Magee | Mrs. Moreno | Ms. Meyers | Mrs. Maddox | Ms. Mukai |

| Ms. MacKay | Mrs. Miller | Mrs. Mosley | Ms. Moxie | Ms. Mojo |

Name _____

The Mystery Number

Merlin the magician has a mystery number under his hat. Use the clues to eliminate one number at a time until you find Merlin's mystery number.

The second numeral of the mystery number is odd.

The mystery number has more than five digits.

The mystery number contains at least one 7.

The mystery number lacks the numeral 3.

The mystery number has the same numeral twice in a row.

The mystery number is even.

The mystery number is missing the numeral 1.

The mystery number does not have more than six digits.

20

Name _____

The Mystery Number

Merlin's mystery number is _____

251,172

457,732

259,962

860,076

476,604

47,664

678,246

6,722,456

597,785

Name _____

Pick a Pet

The López family has decided to get a new pet, but everybody wants something special. Which pet does the family choose? Use the clues to help you eliminate one animal at a time.

I don't want a furry pet that likes to run around on an exercise wheel. The noise will keep me awake at night!

I don't want a pet that has gills.

I'm afraid of eight-legged animals!

I don't want a pet that can fly away if someone leaves a door open .

I don't like any creature that doesn't have legs and can slither away.

We don't have a large back yard, and our house is too small for a large animal.

I don't want a pet I have to walk every day.

I don't want it to hop out of its hutch and get away.

I don't want a pet that has a hard shell. I prefer a soft, fluffy animal.

22

Name _____

Pick a Pet

The name of the pet the Lopez family selected is _____

Fluffy

Spidey

Sunny

Goldie

Noah

Myrtle

Max

Pepe

Roxie

Tony

23

Name _____

The New Car

Mom's ready to buy a new car. She's made a list of things to consider when shopping for her car. Use the clues to help eliminate one car at a time until only one car is left.

I like the feel of the sun on my face while I drive.

I need to be able to see cars behind me on both sides of my new car.

My new car needs to have a very simple paint job that won't compete with its style.

I don't own a boat or trailer to tow around.

I would never buy a car that has the name of a bird.

I want good radio reception so I can listen to music while I drive.

I want the back end of the car to look very stylish.

I want a car with seats that won't show the dirt.

I want wheels with a sporty look.

Name _____

The New Car

What is the name of the car Mom buys? _____

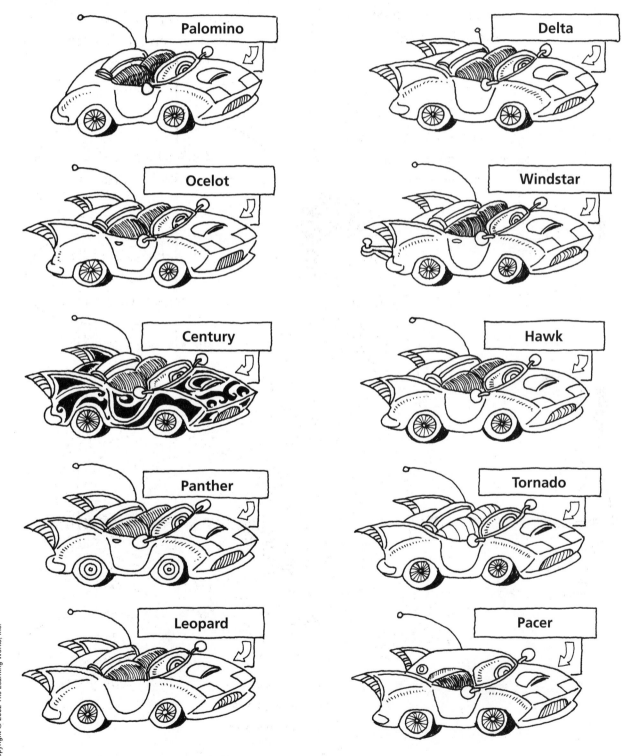

25

Name _____

Charlie the Champ

Charlie is a champ, but it's up to you to discover the sport in which he excels.
Use the clues to eliminate one sport at a time.

The term *gutter ball* is not used in Charlie's sport.

The word *puck* is not used in the sport Charlie plays.

The term *takedown* is not used in Charlie's sport.

The word *knockout* is not used in Charlie's sport.

The word *spike* is not used in the sport Charlie plays.

You will not hear the word *tackle* during one of Charlie's games.

The word *target* is not part of Charlie's sport.

Charlie's sport does not use the term *love*.

The word *hoop* is not used in Charlie's sport.

26

Name _____

Charlie the Champ

The sport in which Charlie is a champ is _____

Ice Hockey **Football** **Soccer**

Volleyball **Bowling** **Basketball** **Archery**

Wrestling **Tennis** **Boxing**

27

Name _____

Who's Not in the Zoo?

Help! An animal has escaped from the city zoo! See if you can discover which animal is missing by using the clues to eliminate one animal at a time.

The animal that is missing did not fly away.

The animal that is missing has neither horns nor antlers.

The animal that is on the loose does not like to swing from tree to tree.

The missing animal is not a pachyderm.

The animal that is missing is not a reptile.

The animal that is missing is not a marsupial that carries its young in a pouch.

The missing animal does not have young called lambs.

The runaway animal does not wade in streams in search of fish.

The missing animal does not eat insects with its long, sticky tongue.

Name _____

Who's Not in the Zoo?

The animal that has escaped from the zoo is the_____

Parrot

Python

Spider Monkey

Sheep

Anteater

Giraffe

Tiger

Kangaroo

Elephant

Bear

29

Name _____

Choose Sue's Shoes

After trying on lots and lots of footwear, Sue is about to make her decision!
What kind of footwear will she get? Use the clues to eliminate
one answer at a time to discover which shoes she'll choose.

I don't need shoes to wear to the beach and
in the water when there are a lot of pebbles and sharp rocks.

Soccer season is over for the year, so I don't need any shoes for that sport.

I don't need any dressy shoes, especially ones that are hard to walk in.

I just took up a new sport, but I already have special shoes
to help me keep my balance when I tee off.

I don't need footwear to wear in the evening when I'm
lounging around the house in my robe.

I just finished running a half-marathon, and the shoes I wore are still perfectly good.

My dance classes are over for now,
and my shoes will last for another round of classes next spring.

I don't need shoes to protect my feet from snakes or poison ivy.

The weather should be bright and sunny for the next few months,
so I don't have to worry about protecting my shoes from bad weather.

I already have too many open-air shoes with low heels
to wear in the summer, and I don't need more.

30

Name _____

Choose Sue's Shoes

Which shoes will Sue choose? _____

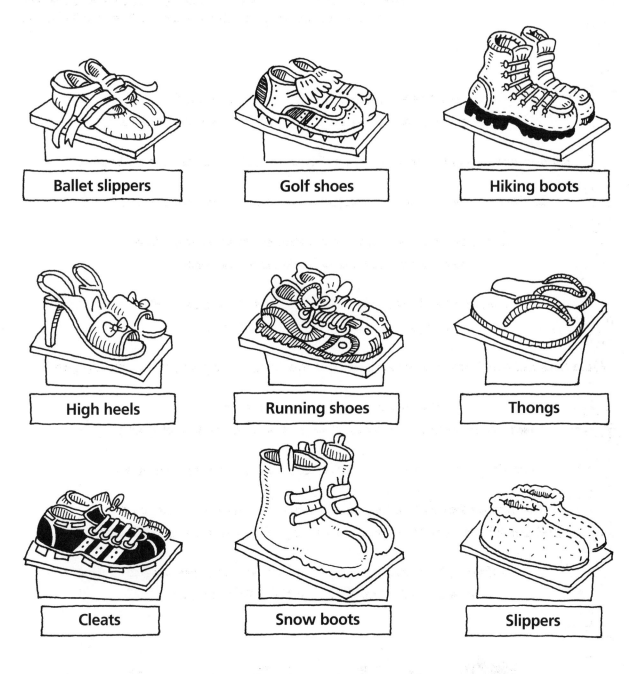

Ballet slippers

Golf shoes

Hiking boots

High heels

Running shoes

Thongs

Cleats

Snow boots

Slippers

Loafers

Sandals

Name _____

Catch the Crook

Someone just robbed Precious Gems, a jewelry store in the mall! The thief got away with thousands of dollars worth of diamonds. Police were called to the scene to get descriptions from eye witnesses. Catch the crook by using the clues to eliminate one suspect at a time until the crook is caught.

The crook looked like he just went to the barber for a buzz.

There was no way to tell if the crook had a tattoo on his arm.

The crook's cap almost flew off as he ran away.

It didn't take the crook long to throw a shirt on in the morning.

The crook had no place to hide any jewels in his shirt.

The thief was very agile, and he could run very fast.

He could make a quick getaway because of his running shoes.

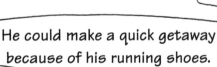

The robber had good vision.

He must have chosen his socks in the dark this morning.

Name _____

Catch the Crook

The name of the thief is _____

Beau   **Moe**   **Joe**   **Fred**   **Red**

Ted   **Ned**   **Mack**   **Jack**   **Zack**

33

Name _____

Vacation Time

Where is the Davis family going on vacation? Find the name of the state by using the clues to eliminate one state at a time.

The state is not mostly desert.

There are no igloos found in the state.

The state is not nicknamed the Beehive State.

The state is not known for volcanoes and pineapple.

The state is not the home of the Golden Gate Bridge.

The state they plan to visit is not on the Atlantic coast.

The state is not named after a United States president.

The state is not north of Missouri and south of Minnesota.

The state does not border the Gulf of Mexico on the south.

Name _____

Vacation Time

What state is the Davis family going to visit? _____

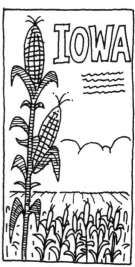

Name _____

Franny's Favorite Book

Franny loves to read. See if you can identify her favorite book by using the clues to eliminate one at a time.

Franny's favorite book is not about an animal.

Franny's favorite book is not a biography.

Franny isn't into science fiction.

Franny's favorite book is not a historical fiction.

Franny's favorite book is not a how-to book.

Franny's favorite book is not an autobiography.

Franny doesn't like to cook.

Franny's favorite book is not a mystery.

Franny's least favorite subject in school is math.

Name _____

Franny's Favorite Book

The title of Franny's favorite book is _____

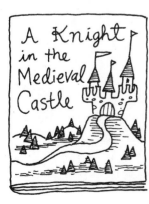

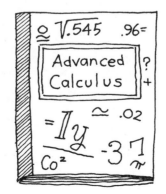

37

Name _____

Goodness Snakes—Who's Jake?

Who's Jake? Discover which snake in the zoo is Jake by using the clues to eliminate one reptile at a time. The snake that's left is Jake.

Jake the snake is related to the python and is pale brown with dark marks on his back.

Jake is not a snake whose name contains the name of a part of the human body.

Jake is not a snake whose name contains the name of a beverage.

Jake is not a snake whose name is also that of a vegetable.

Jake the snake does not have markings that look like rings.

Jake the snake does not have a name that implies royalty.

Jake is not a snake who makes a noise when frightened.

Part of Jake's head does not expand when he's upset.

Jake is not a snake that has a long stripe on his body.

38

Name _____

Goodness Snakes—Who's Jake?

What kind of snake is Jake? _____

39

Name _____

Casey's Career

Casey is looking for a new career and has narrowed his choices down to ten jobs.
Use the clues to eliminate one job at a time. What career does Casey choose?

When I'm around plants or flowers, I can't stop sneezing.
My eyes itch, and I break out in a rash.

Math was never my best subject in school, and I wouldn't enjoy
working with numbers all day long.

I'm too old to be prancing around a stage dressed in tights.

The sight of blood makes me squeamish and faint.

I get car sick very easily and hate driving in traffic.

I don't want to wear a heavy uniform, helmet, and boots —
especially on hot days.

I can't draw very well and am color blind.

I'm allergic to cats and dogs and other furry creatures.

I wouldn't want to be around food all day
because I'd eat too much.

40

Name _____

Casey's Career

What occupation does Casey choose? _____

Taxi Driver

Accountant

Artist

Florist

Veterinarian

Surgeon

Chef

Ballet Dancer

Teacher

Fire Fighter

41

Name _____

Pick a President

Jenny is doing a report on a U.S. president. Use the clues to help you eliminate one name at a time to find the subject of her report.

The president's last name is not the name of a car.

The president I chose does not go by the nickname of Bill.

This person was not the first president of the United States.

The president I chose was not married to a woman named Lady Bird.

The subject of my report did not sign the Declaration of Independence.

The subject of my report was not the thirty-fourth president of the United States.

The president I chose was not assassinated while driving in a motorcade in Dallas, Texas.

The president I selected did not have a father who was also president of the United States.

42

Name _____

Pick a President

Jenny is writing her report on President _____

Lyndon Johnson

William Clinton

Harry S. Truman

George W. Bush

John F. Kennedy

George Washington

Gerald Ford

Dwight D. Eisenhower

Thomas Jefferson

Name _____

How Does Your Garden Grow?

Many vegetables grow in Mr. Marden's garden. Find the vegetable that is *not* in his garden by using the clues to eliminate one veggie at a time.

The missing vegetable is not the thick part of an underground stem called a tuber.

The vegetable that is missing does not come from the stalk or stem of a plant.

The vegetable that is missing from his garden is not used to make pickles.

The vegetable that is missing is not the main ingredient in Caesar salads.

The vegetable that is missing does not come from the root of the plant.

The missing vegetable is not mixed with corn to make succotash.

The vegetable that is missing doesn't come from the plant's leaf.

The missing vegetable is not grown from a bulb.

The missing vegetable doesn't grow in a pod.

44

Name _____

How Does Your Garden Grow?

What vegetable is missing from Mr. Marden's garden? _____

45

Name _____

Name That Year

In what year was Mike, the famous rock star, born?
Use the clues to eliminate one year at a time.

Mike was born between the years 1930 and 2001.

Mike was born in a year greater than the number 1,935 but less than the number 1,999.

No numerals are duplicated in the year Mike was born.

Mike was born between the years 1940 and 1998.

There are no zeroes in the year Mike was born.

Mike was born in an even-numbered year.

Mike was born between the years 1965 and 1980.

Mike was born between the years 1971 and 1981.

Mike was born in a year that is greater than the number 1,951 but less than the number 1,983.

Name _____

Name That Year

In what year was Mike born? _____

Name _____

Answer Key

Pages 6–7 The Dog Show: Roxie

Pages 8–9 Samantha's New Hat: $18.95

Pages 10–11 For the Birds: #6

Pages 12–13 Now Playing: Home Alone #98

Pages 14–15 What's for Dessert?: Cookies

Pages 16–17 The Toy Store: Board game Panache

Pages 18–19 The Substitute Teacher: Ms. Mukai

Pages 20–21 The Mystery Number: 476,604

Pages 22–23 Pick a Pet: Max, the cat

Pages 24–25 The New Car: Ocelot

Pages 26–27 Charlie the Champ: Soccer

Pages 28–29 Who's Not in the Zoo?: Tiger

Pages 30–31 Choose Sue's Shoes: Loafers

Pages 32–33 Catch the Crook: Ned

Pages 34–35 Vacation Time: Colorado

Pages 36–37 Franny's Favorite Book: *New Kid on the Block*

Pages 38–39 Goodness Snakes—Who's Jake?: Python

Pages 40–41 Casey's Career: Teacher

Pages 42–43 Pick a President: Harry S. Truman

Pages 44–45 How Does Your Garden Grow?: Turnips

Pages 46–47 Name That Year: 1978